Andrew Brodie Basics

LET'S DO ADDITION AND SUBTRACTION

FOR AGES 8-9

with over **100** reward stickers

- Over 400 practice questions
- Regular progress tests
- Extra quick-fire questions and handy tips

Published 2016 by Bloomsbury Publishing Plc
50 Bedford Square, London, WC1B 3DP

www.bloomsbury.com

ISBN 978–14729–2624–1

Copyright © 2016 Bloomsbury Publishing
Text copyright © 2016 Andrew Brodie
Cover and inside illustrations of Pippa the Penguin and Andrew Brodie
© 2016 Nikalas Catlow. Other inside illustrations © 2016 Cathy Hughes

A CIP catalogue for this book is available from the British Library.

10 9 8 7 6 5 4 3 2 1

Printed in China by Leo Paper Products

This book is produced using paper that is made from wood grown in managed, sustainable forests. It is natural, renewable and recyclable. The logging and manufacturing processes conform to the environmental regulations of the country of origin.

To see our full range of titles visit **www.bloomsbury.com**

B L O O M S B U R Y

Introduction

This is the fourth in the series of Andrew Brodie *Let's Do Addition and Subtraction* books. The book contains more than 400 mental maths questions, deliberately designed to cover the following key aspects of the 'Number' section of the National Curriculum:

- Number and place value
- Addition and subtraction

Your child will benefit most greatly if you have the opportunity to discuss the questions with them. You may find that your child gains low scores when they first begin to take the tests. Make sure that they don't lose confidence. Instead, encourage them to learn from their mistakes.

The level of difficulty increases gradually throughout the book, but note that some questions are repeated. For example, addition facts where the total is up to 20, together with the related subtraction facts, will appear lots of times. Similarly, there will be lots of practice of combinations of numbers that total one hundred. This is to ensure that pupils have

the opportunity to learn vital new facts: they may not know the answer to a particular question the first time they encounter it, but this provides the opportunity for you to help them to learn it for the next time that they come across it. Don't be surprised if they need to practise certain questions many times.

Children of this age will continue practising addition and subtraction of numbers with up to three digits mentally. They will add and subtract numbers with up to four digits, using columns for formal written methods. They should be encouraged to estimate answers before calculating, and to check their answers. They can check additions by subtracting and check subtractions by adding. For example, 100 take away 67 equals 33, because 67 plus 33 equals 100.

Children gain confidence by learning facts that they can use in their future work. With lots of practice they will see their score improve and will learn to find maths both satisfying and enjoyable.

Look out for...

Pippa the Penguin, who provides useful tips and helpful advice.

Brodie's Fast Five, quick-fire questions designed to test your child's mental arithmetic.

Addition speed

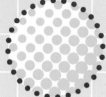

Time yourself answering these questions. Try to get faster with each set.

Set A

1	9 + 4 =
2	7 + 6 =
3	8 + 8 =
4	5 + 7 =
5	6 + 8 =
6	9 + 7 =
7	4 + 8 =
8	7 + 7 =
9	3 + 9 =
10	8 + 3 =
11	12 + 4 =
12	11 + 8 =
13	13 + 3 =
14	14 + 5 =
15	12 + 6 =

Set B

1	6 + 4 =
2	5 + 6 =
3	9 + 8 =
4	3 + 7 =
5	7 + 8 =
6	2 + 7 =
7	5 + 8 =
8	9 + 7 =
9	4 + 9 =
10	9 + 3 =
11	15 + 4 =
12	17 + 8 =
13	12 + 3 =
14	16 + 5 =
15	13 + 6 =

Set C

1	9 + 9 =
2	7 + 5 =
3	8 + 3 =
4	5 + 8 =
5	6 + 2 =
6	9 + 6 =
7	4 + 5 =
8	7 + 9 =
9	3 + 8 =
10	8 + 5 =
11	12 + 5 =
12	11 + 3 =
13	13 + 6 =
14	14 + 6 =
15	12 + 9 =

Time taken — Seconds

Time taken — Seconds

Time taken — Seconds

Subtraction speed

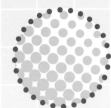

Time yourself answering these questions. Try to get faster with each set.

Set A

1	9 – 3 =	
2	12 – 5 =	
3	16 – 9 =	
4	18 – 7 =	
5	8 – 5 =	
6	10 – 6 =	
7	11 – 4 =	
8	13 – 6 =	
9	15 – 9 =	
10	14 – 8 =	
11	21 – 7 =	
12	23 – 5 =	
13	27 – 9 =	
14	25 – 6 =	
15	22 – 8 =	

Set B

1	18 – 3 =	
2	13 – 5 =	
3	17 – 9 =	
4	11 – 7 =	
5	14 – 5 =	
6	9 – 6 =	
7	10 – 4 =	
8	12 – 6 =	
9	11 – 9 =	
10	23 – 8 =	
11	25 – 7 =	
12	29 – 5 =	
13	30 – 9 =	
14	22 – 6 =	
15	24 – 8 =	

Set C

1	9 – 5 =	
2	12 – 7 =	
3	16 – 4 =	
4	18 – 9 =	
5	8 – 8 =	
6	10 – 3 =	
7	11 – 8 =	
8	13 – 5 =	
9	15 – 7 =	
10	14 – 6 =	
11	21 – 3 =	
12	23 – 6 =	
13	27 – 11 =	
14	25 – 9 =	
15	22 – 7 =	

Time taken — Seconds

Time taken — Seconds

Time taken — Seco...

Can you write the missing answers in each square?

dd the numbers in the left column to the umbers in the top row. Some of the answers in he first addition square have been done for you. ime how long you take to complete each square.

1

+	8	6	7	9
5		11		
8				
7	15			
9			18	

Time taken — Seconds

3

+	7	9	6	8
6				
8				
7				
9				

Time taken — Seconds

2

+	17	18	19	20
13				
14				
15				
16				

Time taken — Seconds

4

+	14	15	16	17
14				
15				
16				
17				

Time taken — Seconds

Brodie's Fast Five

63 + 17 =   59 + 11 =

46 + 14 =   38 + 12 =   77 + 13 =

Subtraction squares

Can you write the missing answers in each square?

Subtract the numbers in the left column from the numbers in the top row. Some of the answers in the first subtraction square have been done for you. Time how long you take to complete each square.

1

–	12	13	14	15
6		7		
8				
10	2			
12				3

3

–	16	17	18	19
7				
9				
11				
13				

2

–	19	21	23	20
12				
6				
8				
14				

4

–	17	18	19	20
11				
13				
15				
17				

Brodie's Fast Five

50 – 13 =

100 – 17 =

80 – 16 =

60 – 26 =

70 – 15 =

Addition and subtraction

Remember to look for the addition sign or the subtraction sign.

You can use the number line to help you if you want to.

5 10 15 20 25 30 35 40 45 50 55 60 65 70 75 80 85 90 95 100

1   $38 + 47 =$

2   26 more than 53 =

3   37 less than 65 =

4   Add together sixty–three and twenty-eight.

5   Take thirty-seven away from eighty-two.

6   What is the total of forty-seven, thirteen and twenty-six?

7   What is seventy-one take away twenty-five?

8   Double forty-five.

9   $9 + 8 + 7 =$

0   $19 + 8 + 7 =$

1   $19 + 18 + 7 =$

2   $19 + 18 + 17 =$

3   $100 - 51 =$

4   $100 - 26 =$

5   Double 53 =

Brodie's Fast Five

$100 - 72 =$ $100 - 52 =$

$100 - 84 =$ $100 - 64 =$ $100 - 32 =$

7

**Look carefully at the sign for each question.
Is it an addition or a subtraction?**

1	9 – 5 =
2	12 + 5 =
3	16 – 7 =
4	18 + 7 =
5	10 – 5 =
6	10 + 26 =
7	11 – 7 =
8	13 + 6 =
9	21 – 9 =
10	14 + 8 =
11	21 – 6 =
12	23 + 5 =
13	22 – 9 =
14	25 + 6 =
15	20 – 8 =

16	18 + 3 =
17	22 – 5 =
18	17 + 9 =
19	23 – 7 =
20	14 + 5 =
21	21 – 6 =
22	10 – 7 =
23	12 + 6 =
24	11 + 9 =
25	23 – 0 =
26	25 + 7 =
27	29 – 12 =
28	30 – 7 =
29	22 + 6 =
30	24 + 8 =

31	13 – 5 =
32	12 + 7 =
33	16 – 9 =
34	18 + 9 =
35	18 – 6 =
36	30 – 3 =
37	13 + 8 =
38	23 – 5 =
39	15 + 7 =
40	14 – 8 =
41	21 + 9 =
42	23 – 11 =
43	27 + 11 =
44	25 – 16 =
45	22 + 7 =

46

+	12	14	16	18
11				
13				
15				
17				

47

–	17	18	19	20
12				
16				
14				
13				

Adding to find missing numbers

Can you find the missing numbers?

You can use the number line to help you if you want to.

5 10 15 20 25 30 35 40 45 50 55 60 65 70 75 80 85 90 95 100

1 16 + [   ] = 100

2 23 + [   ] = 100

3 19 + [   ] = 100

4 12 + [   ] = 100

5 44 + [   ] = 100

6 31 + [   ] = 100

7 25 + [   ] = 100

8 48 + [   ] = 100

9 37 + [   ] = 100

10 49 + [   ] = 100

11 36 + [   ] = 100

12 52 + [   ] = 100

13 33 + [   ] = 100

14 18 + [   ] = 100

15 29 + [   ] = 100

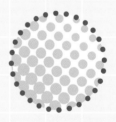

Brodie's Fast Five

135 + 7 =   489 + 11 =

267 + 9 =   567 + 8 =   399 + 5 =

Subtracting to find missing numbers

Can you find the missing numbers?

You can use the number line to help you if you want to.

0 5 **10** 15 **20** 25 **30** 35 **40** 45 **50** 55 **60** 65 **70** 75 **80** 85 **90** 95 **100**

1 100 – ___ = 23

2 100 – ___ = 17

3 100 – ___ = 25

4 100 – ___ = 51

5 100 – ___ = 33

6 100 – ___ = 43

7 100 – ___ = 53

8 100 – ___ = 75

9 100 – ___ = 81

10 100 – ___ = 63

11 100 – ___ = 73

12 100 – ___ = 83

13 100 – ___ = 59

14 100 – ___ = 88

15 100 – ___ = 39

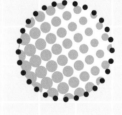

Brodie's Fast Five

123 – 14 = ___   224 – 17 = ___

324 – 18 = ___   425 – 19 = ___   522 – 16 = ___

Complete the addition square as fast as you can.

Add the numbers in the left column to the numbers in the top row. Some are done for you. Time how long you take to complete the square.

+	23	25	27	29	22	24	26	28	21
13		38							
15									
17									
19				48					
12									
14									
16									
18								46	
11									

Time taken
Seconds

Brodie's Fast Five

35 + _____ = 90   _____ + 47 = 90

22 + _____ = 90   _____ + 45 = 90   72 + _____ = 90

Subtraction square

Complete the subtraction square as fast as you can.

Subtract the numbers in the left column from the numbers in the top row. Some are done for you. Time how long you take to complete the square.

−	20	30	40	50	60	70	80	90	100
12		18							
13									
14									
15				35					
16									
17									
18									
19								71	
20									

Time taken Seconds

Brodie's Fast Five

80 − [ ] = 25   [ ] − 42 = 53

72 − [ ] = 44   [ ] − 29 = 21   91 − [ ] = 25

Addition and subtraction

Do you know that additions and subtractions are related to each other?

Look at four calculations using the numbers 28, 53 and 81.

Additions: $28 + 53 = 81$ and $53 + 28 = 81$

Subtractions: $81 - 28 = 53$ and $81 - 53 = 28$

1   Write four calculations using the numbers 28, 73 and 101.

Additions:

Subtractions:

2   Write four calculations using the numbers 68, 52 and 120.

Additions:

Subtractions:

3   Find two different numbers that add together to make 130.
Write four calculations using these numbers.

Additions:

Subtractions:

4   Find two different numbers that add together to make 144.
Write four calculations using these numbers.

Additions:

Subtractions:

Brodie's Fast Five

$102 - 14 =$ $95 + 25 =$

$97 + 24 =$ $110 - 31 =$ $92 + 49 =$

Addition

1   36   +   = 110

2   19   +   = 110

3   47   +   = 110

4   13   +   = 110

5   52   +   = 110

Subtraction

6   110 −   = 77

7   110 −   = 59

8   110 −   = 48

9   110 −   = 36

10   110 −   = 64

11   Find two different numbers that add together to make 121.
Write four calculations using these numbers.

Additions:

Subtractions:

12   Find two different numbers that add together to make 149.
Write four calculations using these numbers.

Additions:

Subtractions:

Adding three numbers

You need to try these questions mentally.

Set A

1. 7 + 8 + 4 =
2. 7 + 5 + 6 =
3. 3 + 8 + 8 =
4. 5 + 7 + 9 =
5. 4 + 6 + 8 =
6. 9 + 7 + 5 =
7. 8 + 8 + 8 =
8. 7 + 7 + 7 =
9. 3 + 9 + 9 =
10. 8 + 7 + 6 =
11. 12 + 14 + 13 =
12. 11 + 13 + 15 =
13. 13 + 14 + 15 =
14. 14 + 15 + 16 =
15. 12 + 16 + 11 =

Set B

1. 5 + 8 + 9 =
2. 3 + 9 + 6 =
3. 3 + 6 + 9 =
4. 5 + 9 + 11 =
5. 9 + 6 + 8 =
6. 3 + 7 + 5 =
7. 7 + 4 + 9 =
8. 6 + 6 + 6 =
9. 8 + 2 + 12 =
10. 5 + 7 + 6 =
11. 15 + 14 + 13 =
12. 13 + 13 + 13 =
13. 14 + 14 + 14 =
14. 15 + 15 + 15 =
15. 16 + 16 + 16 =

Set C

1. 9 + 8 + 7 =
2. 7 + 3 + 9 =
3. 6 + 8 + 2 =
4. 12 + 7 + 9 =
5. 5 + 6 + 11 =
6. 2 + 12 + 12 =
7. 5 + 8 + 6 =
8. 9 + 2 + 8 =
9. 7 + 9 + 6 =
10. 12 + 12 + 6 =
11. 16 + 14 + 16 =
12. 17 + 13 + 15 =
13. 16 + 14 + 20 =
14. 25 + 15 + 35 =
15. 25 + 25 + 25 =

Time taken · Seconds

Time taken · Seconds

Time taken · Seconds

Addition and subtraction

Do you remember what 'mentally' means?

In each question add the first two numbers then subtract the third.

Set A

1. $7 + 8 - 6 =$
2. $7 + 9 - 5 =$
3. $12 + 8 - 7 =$
4. $15 + 7 - 4 =$
5. $14 + 6 - 9 =$
6. $9 + 7 - 8 =$
7. $8 + 8 - 4 =$
8. $12 + 7 - 5 =$
9. $11 + 9 - 6 =$
10. $18 + 7 - 9 =$
11. $12 + 14 - 4 =$
12. $12 + 13 - 8 =$
13. $16 + 14 - 12 =$
14. $25 + 15 - 14 =$
15. $12 + 18 - 4 =$

Set B

1. $17 + 8 - 9 =$
2. $7 + 19 - 8 =$
3. $12 + 18 - 11 =$
4. $12 + 6 - 8 =$
5. $14 + 16 - 15 =$
6. $19 + 7 - 10 =$
7. $8 + 18 - 12 =$
8. $19 + 9 - 5 =$
9. $15 + 9 - 16 =$
10. $18 + 17 - 9 =$
11. $16 + 14 - 4 =$
12. $17 + 13 - 8 =$
13. $12 + 18 - 12 =$
14. $35 + 35 - 14 =$
15. $22 + 22 - 44 =$

Set C

1. $7 + 18 - 9 =$
2. $12 + 9 - 5 =$
3. $14 + 8 - 7 =$
4. $15 + 8 - 4 =$
5. $16 + 6 - 8 =$
6. $19 + 17 - 11 =$
7. $14 + 14 - 15 =$
8. $12 + 12 - 5 =$
9. $11 + 11 - 8 =$
10. $18 + 18 - 13 =$
11. $13 + 13 - 11 =$
12. $15 + 15 - 12 =$
13. $16 + 16 - 12 =$
14. $45 + 45 - 28 =$
15. $55 + 55 - 18 =$

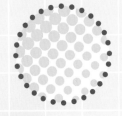

Time taken
Seconds

Time taken
Seconds

Time taken
Seconds

Adding multiples of ten

These questions need to be done mentally, too!

Set A

1	70 + 40 =
2	60 + 60 =
3	90 + 80 =
4	30 + 90 =
5	80 + 80 =
6	60 + 70 =
7	50 + 80 =
8	90 + 70 =
9	30 + 80 =
10	40 + 60 =
11	130 + 140 =
12	110 + 180 =
13	180 + 130 =
14	190 + 160 =
15	180 + 180 =

Set B

1	80 + 30 =
2	70 + 60 =
3	120 + 60 =
4	40 + 70 =
5	70 + 80 =
6	110 + 90 =
7	150 + 50 =
8	120 + 80 =
9	60 + 140 =
10	130 + 70 =
11	120 + 180 =
12	170 + 130 =
13	140 + 160 =
14	110 + 190 =
15	150 + 150 =

Set C

1	90 + 90 =
2	70 + 70 =
3	80 + 80 =
4	60 + 60 =
5	110 + 110 =
6	150 + 150 =
7	120 + 120 =
8	140 + 140 =
9	160 + 160 =
10	130 + 130 =
11	170 + 170 =
12	190 + 190 =
13	180 + 180 =
14	200 + 200 =
15	250 + 250 =

Time taken
Seconds

Time taken
Seconds

Time taken
Seconds

Subtracting multiples of ten

More mental questions! Are you getting good at them?

Set A

1. 190 – 30 =
2. 170 – 110 =
3. 160 – 90 =
4. 180 – 90 =
5. 120 – 50 =
6. 130 – 80 =
7. 110 – 40 =
8. 270 – 60 =
9. 350 – 90 =
10. 720 – 80 =
11. 210 – 70 =
12. 480 – 150 =
13. 660 – 90 =
14. 830 – 60 =
15. 910 – 80 =

Set B

1. 180 – 30 =
2. 230 – 50 =
3. 490 – 110 =
4. 620 – 70 =
5. 930 – 50 =
6. 710 – 60 =
7. 550 – 80 =
8. 360 – 70 =
9. 540 – 90 =
10. 460 – 80 =
11. 250 – 70 =
12. 740 – 150 =
13. 360 – 180 =
14. 820 – 160 =
15. 900 – 450 =

Set C

1. 190 – 60 =
2. 140 – 70 =
3. 160 – 80 =
4. 120 – 60 =
5. 180 – 90 =
6. 220 – 110 =
7. 240 – 120 =
8. 480 – 240 =
9. 660 – 330 =
10. 840 – 420 =
11. 400 – 120 =
12. 600 – 160 =
13. 900 – 340 =
14. 800 – 370 =
15. 500 – 250 =

Time taken — Seconds

Time taken — Seconds

Time taken — Seconds

Adding and subtracting hundreds to and from three-digit numbers

You'll probably find these mental arithmetic questions quite easy!

Adding

You need to be able to add hundreds to three-digit numbers. How quickly can you answer the questions?

1. 479 + 300 =
2. 389 + 200 =
3. 624 + 400 =
4. 438 + 300 =
5. 842 + 500 =
6. 269 + 600 =
7. 835 + 500 =
8. 442 + 400 =
9. 583 + 300 =
10. 679 + 800 =

Subtracting

You need to be able to subtract hundreds from three-digit numbers.

1. 747 – 200 =
2. 832 – 500 =
3. 916 – 400 =
4. 803 – 600 =
5. 932 – 900 =
6. 891 – 500 =
7. 789 – 600 =
8. 666 – 300 =
9. 713 – 400 =
10. 863 – 200 =

Time taken — Seconds

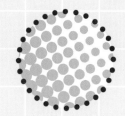

Time taken — Seconds

Brodie's Fast Five

297 + 400 =   765 + 500 =

826 – 200 =   1000 – 420 =   913 + 400 =

19

Look carefully at each question. Look at the numbers.

Look at the sign. Is it an add sign or a subtract sign?

1 $12 + 8 - 6 =$

2 $14 + 9 - 5 =$

3 $12 + 8 - 13 =$

4 $26 + 7 - 4 =$

5 $24 + 8 - 9 =$

6 $26 + 7 - 8 =$

7 $38 + 8 - 14 =$

8 $32 + 7 - 15 =$

9 $35 + 9 - 6 =$

10 $48 + 7 - 9 =$

11 $130 + 80 =$

12 $160 + 140 =$

13 $130 + 170 =$

14 $320 + 180 =$

15 $270 + 150 =$

16 $340 - 110 =$

17 $240 - 160 =$

18 $480 - 190 =$

19 $520 - 330 =$

20 $710 - 420 =$

21 $564 - 200 =$

22 $888 - 400 =$

23 $907 - 300 =$

24 $742 - 500 =$

25 $635 - 300 =$

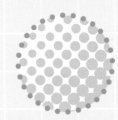

Read the explanation on this page very carefully.

Look at these numbers:

5   6   2   3

There are   There are   There are   There is
five tens.   six units.   two tens.   three units.

To add 56 and 23 we can write them one above the other. We say that the 6 and the 3 are in the units column. The 5 and the 2 are in the tens column.

```
    5   6              5   6              5   6
+   2   3          +   2   3          +   2   3
_____          _____          _____
                       9              7   9
```

We add the   Then we add the tens to
units first.   get the final answer.

Sometimes there are enough units to make an extra ten.

```
    3   9              3   9              3   9
+   2   5          +   2   5          +   2   5
_____          _____          _____
                       4              6   4
                   1                  1
```

9 units + 5 units is enough   Then we add all the tens,
to make a ten and 4 units   including the extra one to
because 9 + 5 = 14.   get the final answer.

Addition in columns

It's your chance to write additions in columns.

Answer these questions using columns for your working. The first one is done for you.

1 72 + 23

```
    7  2
+   2  3
───────
    9  5
```

2 43 + 35

3 31 + 28

4 56 + 35

5 67 + 23

6 44 + 32

7 39 + 26

8 64 + 18

9 51 + 35

10 47 + 38

Brodie's Fast Five

57 + 30 =

57 + 230 =

57 + 130 =

57 + 330 =

57 + 430 =

Sometimes two two-digit numbers add up to more than 100.

Sometimes there are enough units to make an extra ten and sometimes there are enough tens to make an extra hundred.

```
      7  9            7  9            7  9            7  9
  +   4  6        +   4  6        +   4  6        +   4  6
  ─────────       ─────────       ─────────       ─────────
                         5            2  5         1  2  5
                      1               1  1         1  1
```

9 units + 6 units is enough to make a ten and 5 units because 9 + 6 = 15.

Then we add all the tens, including the extra one.

We had enough tens to make a hundred.

Now try these.

1 84 + 38

3 95 + 69

2 73 + 42

4 75 + 75

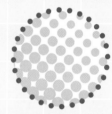

Brodie's Fast Five

6 +   = 19   + 13 = 19

12 +   = 19   + 7 = 19   9 +   = 19

Read the explanation on this page very carefully.

Look at these numbers:

8   7   2   3

There are   There are   There are   There are
eight tens.   seven units.   two tens.   three units.

To subtract 23 from 87 we can write the 87 above the 23. We say that the
7 and the 3 are in the units column. The 8 and the 2 are in the tens column.

```
    8   7              8   7              8   7
-   2   3          -   2   3          -   2   3
_____         _____         _____
                       4              6   4
```

We subtract the 3 units   Then we subtract the
from the 7 units first.   2 tens from the 8 tens.

Sometimes there are not enough units in the top number, so we break
one of the tens into ten extra units then do the subtraction.

We use one of the 7 tens to   Then we subtract the
make ten extra units so now   tens to get the final
we have 14 units and can   answer.
subtract the 8 units.

```
                        6   1              6   1
    7   4               7̸   4              7̸   4
-   3   8          -   3   8          -   3   8
_____         _____         _____
                            8          3   6
```

Subtraction in columns

It's your chance to write subtractions in columns.

Use columns to find the answers to these questions.

1 86 – 42

2 98 – 56

3 47 – 31

4 69 – 22

5 75 – 34

6 51 – 26

7 85 – 48

8 93 – 62

9 90 – 56

10 62 – 37

Brodie's Fast Five

350 – 5 =   350 – 25 =

350 – 15 =   350 – 35 =   350 – 45 =

25

Use columns to find the answers to these questions.

1 53 + 32 =

2 69 + 27 =

3 74 + 25 =

4 56 + 27 =

5 89 – 28 =

6 78 – 35 =

7 63 – 49 =

8 81 – 57 =

9 There are 53 boys and 29 girls. How many children are there altogether?

10 Now there are 27 boys and 82 girls. How many more girls than boys are there?

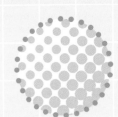

Adding three-digit numbers 1

You need to be able to add three-digit numbers as well as two-digit and one-digit numbers.

1 Add the units.

```
    3  4  6
+   1  3  2
_____
          8
```

2 Add the tens.

```
    3  4  6
+   1  3  2
_____
       7  8
```

3 Add the hundreds.

```
    3  4  6
+   1  3  2
_____
    4  7  8
```

Now try these. Remember, sometimes there are enough units to make an extra ten and sometimes there are enough tens to make an extra hundred.

1 234 + 123

2 561 + 217

3 472 + 326

4 743 + 154

5 312 + 312

6 436 + 128

7 263 + 263

8 180 + 180

Adding three-digit numbers 2

> Sometimes there are enough hundreds to make a thousand.

Sometimes there are enough units to make an extra ten and sometimes there are enough tens to make an extra hundred. Sometimes there are enough hundreds to make a thousand.

1 Add the units.

```
    6  4  7
+   6  4  7
_____
          4
       1
```

2 Add the tens.

```
    6  4  7
+   6  4  7
_____
       9  4
       1
```

3 Add the hundreds.

```
    6  4  7
+   6  4  7
_____
 1  2  9  4
       1
```

1 386 + 295

2 542 + 387

3 472 + 472

4 743 + 444

5 862 + 379

6 750 + 750

7 699 + 699

8 947 + 378

Adding three-digit numbers and two-digit numbers

Always line up the units.

Sometimes we add three-digit and two-digit numbers. Make sure the units digits are in the units column and the tens digits are in the tens column.

1 Add the units.

```
    3  7  9
+      6  8
_____
          7
    1  1
```

2 Add the tens.

```
    3  7  9
+      6  8
_____
       4  7
    1  1
```

3 Add the hundreds.

```
    3  7  9
+      6  8
_____
    4  4  7
    1  1
```

1 475 + 63

5 469 + 28

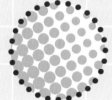

2 637 + 79

6 84 + 862

3 525 + 98

7 74 + 577

4 76 + 632

8 957 + 89

We are going to write this subtraction in columns:

7 1 8 – 2 4 3

Always start with the units. In this subtraction there are enough units in the top number. But there are not enough tens in the top number, so we have to break one of the hundreds to make ten extra tens.

```
        7  1  8              6  1                  6    1
                            7  1  8               7    1  8
     -  2  4  3          -  2  4  3            -   2    4  3
     _____         _____          _____
              5                 7  5                 4  7  5
```

Now try these.

1 586 – 192

4 847 – 264

2 756 – 234

5 946 – 387

3 925 – 367

6 738 – 499

Always line up the units.

ome of the top numbers don't have enough units
o you will need to borrow from the tens.

597 – 146

2 **871 – 236**

3 **952 – 417**

**he top numbers don't have enough tens so you will need
o borrow from the hundreds.**

508 – 137

5 **836 – 475**

6 **627 – 253**

**these questions, the top numbers don't have enough units or enough
ns so you will need to borrow from the tens and the hundreds.**

624 – 179

8 **835 – 266**

9 **925 – 468**

Brodie's Fast Five

200 – 2 =

200 – 22 =

200 – 12 =

200 – 32 =

200 – 42 =

Use columns to find the answers to these questions.

1 572 + 315

6 583 − 329

2 617 + 239

7 612 − 148

3 746 + 88

8 817 − 293

4 869 + 375

9 929 − 359

5 468 − 214

Adding four-digit numbers

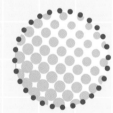

You need to be able to add four-digit numbers as well as three-digit, two-digit and one-digit numbers.

1 Add the units.

```
    2   4   6   5
+   1   3   2   4
─────────────────
                9
```

2 Add the tens.

```
    2   4   6   5
+   1   3   2   4
─────────────────
            8   9
```

3 Add the hundreds.

```
    2   4   6   5
+   1   3   2   4
─────────────────
        7   8   9
```

4 Add the thousands.

```
    2   4   6   5
+   1   3   2   4
─────────────────
    3   7   8   9
```

Now try these. Remember, sometimes there are enough units to make an extra ten, sometimes there are enough tens to make an extra hundred and sometimes there are enough hundreds to make an extra thousand. Sometimes there are even enough thousands to make a ten thousand.

3472 + 2914

4 3945 + 1872

5925 + 3172

5 6823 + 5749

4628 + 2560

6 8750 + 8750

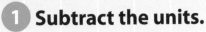
Subtracting four-digit numbers

You need to be able to subtract four-digit numbers as well as three-digit, two-digit and one-digit numbers

1 **Subtract the units.**

```
      5  9  ⁵6̸ ¹8
   -  1  3  5  9
   _____
                 9
```

2 **Subtract the tens.**

```
      5  9  ⁵6̸ ¹8
   -  1  3  5  9
   _____
              0  9
```

3 **Subtract the hundreds.**

```
      5  9  ⁵6̸ ¹8
   -  1  3  5  9
   _____
           6  0  9
```

4 **Subtract the thousands.**

```
      5  9  ⁵6̸ ¹8
   -  1  3  5  9
   _____
        4  6  0  9
```

Now try these. Remember, always start with the units. Sometimes you will need to make extra units from a ten or extra tens from a hundred or extra hundreds from a thousand.

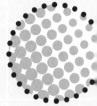

1 6759 – 2345

4 5478 – 2888

2 7399 – 2681

5 9324 – 4687

3 8645 – 3760

6 7309 – 5624

We are going to write this subtraction in columns:

7 0 0 – 3 6 5

1 Subtract the units but there are not enough units so we need to break up a ten. But there are no tens! So we break up a hundred to make ten tens then break up a ten to make ten units. Now we can subtract the units.

2 Subtract the tens. We have nine tens so this is easy.

3 Subtract the hundreds.

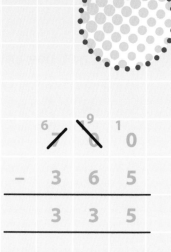

$$
\begin{array}{r}
^6\!\!\!\!\diagup\ ^9\!\!\!\!\diagup\ ^1 0 \\
-\ 3\ 6\ 5 \\
\hline
3\ 3\ 5 \\
\hline
\end{array}
$$

$$
\begin{array}{r}
^6\!\!\!\!\diagup\ ^9\!\!\!\!\diagup\ ^1 0 \\
-\ 3\ 6\ 5 \\
\hline
3\ 3\ 5 \\
\hline
\end{array}
$$

$$
\begin{array}{r}
^6\!\!\!\!\diagup\ ^9\!\!\!\!\diagup\ ^1 0 \\
-\ 3\ 6\ 5 \\
\hline
3\ 3\ 5 \\
\hline
\end{array}
$$

Now try these.

1 600 – 192

3 700 – 367

5 500 – 387

2 800 – 234

4 900 – 264

6 800 – 499

Read the explanation on this page very carefully.

We are going to write this subtraction in columns:

6 0 0 0 − 1 8 7 2

1 Subtract the units. There are not enough units, so we need to break up a ten. But there are no tens and there are no hundreds! So we break up a thousand to make ten hundreds, then a hundred to make ten tens, then break up a ten to make ten units. Now we can subtract the units.

```
  5   9   9   1
  6   0   0   0
−   1   8   7   2
                8
```

2 Subtract the tens. We have nine tens so this is easy.

```
  5   9   9   1
  6   0   0   0
−   1   8   7   2
          2   8
```

3 Subtract the hundreds. We have nine hundreds so this is easy.

```
  5   9   9   1
  6   0   0   0
−   1   8   7   2
      1   2   8
```

4 Subtract the thousands.

```
  5   9   9   1
  6   0   0   0
−   1   8   7   2
  4   1   2   8
```

Now try these.

1 5000 − 2361

2 7000 − 3982

3 8000 − 4738

4 6000 − 3209

5 9000 − 2754

6 8000 − 4994

Addition and subtraction

Decide whether you need addition or subtraction to solve each of these questions.

On its outward journey, an aeroplane flies from London to New York, then from New York to Los Angeles.

On its return journey, the plane flies back to London direct from Los Angeles.

The distance from London to New York is 5576 kilometres.

The distance from New York to Los Angeles is 3940 kilometres.

The distance from Los Angeles to London is 8765 kilometres.

1 How far does the plane travel on altogether on its outward journey?

kilometres

2 How far does the plane fly altogether?

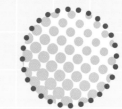

kilometres

3 New York is closer to Los Angeles than it is to London. How much closer?

kilometres

4 How much shorter is the return journey than the outward journey?

kilometres

Use columns to find the answers to these questions.

1 697 + 315

2 892 + 768

3 929 + 88

4 3456 + 6789

5 576 – 214

6 710 – 329

7 2468 – 1708

8 8000 – 3245

9 9000 – 4359

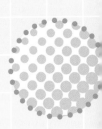

dding decimals

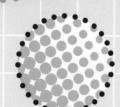

I hope you get the point!

o you know the combinations of tenths that add together o make 1?

0.1 + [   ]

.2 + [   ]

.3 + [   ]

.4 + [   ]

.5 + [   ]

1

0.6 + [   ]

0.7 + [   ]

0.8 + [   ]

0.9 + [   ]

et A

1. $0.2 + 0.4 =$ [   ]
2. $7 + 1.6 =$ [   ]
3. $0.8 + 0.1 =$ [   ]
4. $0.5 + 0.3 =$ [   ]
5. $0.6 + 0.8 =$ [   ]
6. $2.4 + 7 =$ [   ]
7. $1.4 + 0.8 =$ [   ]
8. $0.7 + 0.7 =$ [   ]

Set B

1. $0.6 + 0.4 =$ [   ]
2. $1.5 + 0.6 =$ [   ]
3. $0.9 + 0.8 =$ [   ]
4. $1.3 + 0.5 =$ [   ]
5. $0.7 + 0.8 =$ [   ]
6. $0.2 + 0.7 =$ [   ]
7. $0.5 + 0.8 =$ [   ]
8. $0.9 + 0.7 =$ [   ]

Set C

1. $0.9 + 0.2 =$ [   ]
2. $0.7 + 1.5 =$ [   ]
3. $0.8 + 0.3 =$ [   ]
4. $0.5 + 1.8 =$ [   ]
5. $1.6 + 1.2 =$ [   ]
6. $1.9 + 0.6 =$ [   ]
7. $1.4 + 0.5 =$ [   ]
8. $1.7 + 0.9 =$ [   ]

Time taken — Seconds

Time taken — Seconds

Time taken — Seconds

39

Subtracting decimals

How quickly can you subtract decimals?

Find the missing numbers.

1 – [ ] = 0.3

1 – [ ] = 0.7

1 – [ ] = 0.2

1 – [ ] = 0.1

1 – [ ] = 0.4

1

1 – [ ] = 0.6

1 – [ ] = 0.8

1 – [ ] = 0.5

1 – [ ] = 0.9

Set A

1. $1.2 - 0.4 =$
2. $0.9 - 0.3 =$
3. $1.5 - 0.8 =$
4. $0.8 - 0.4 =$
5. $1.2 - 0.7 =$
6. $0.7 - 0.3 =$
7. $1.6 - 0.9 =$
8. $2.1 - 0.3 =$

Set B

1. $0.6 - 0.4 =$
2. $1.7 - 0.9 =$
3. $2.3 - 0.4 =$
4. $1.8 - 1.2 =$
5. $0.9 - 0.1 =$
6. $3.2 - 0.8 =$
7. $4.5 - 0.7 =$
8. $3.7 - 1.4 =$

Set C

1. $0.9 - 0.2 =$
2. $1.6 - 0.8 =$
3. $2.3 - 1.5 =$
4. $3.4 - 1.6 =$
5. $2.5 - 0.8 =$
6. $3.2 - 1.5 =$
7. $5.5 - 2.7 =$
8. $4.2 - 2.3 =$

Time taken — Seconds

Time taken — Seconds

Time taken — Sec

Adding decimals 2

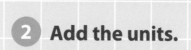

You need to be able to add decimals as well as whole numbers.

1 Add the tenths. There are enough tenths to make an extra unit.

2 Add the units.

```
    4 . 6                4 . 6
+   2 . 8            +   2 . 8
_____          _____
        4                7 . 4
    1                    1
```

Now try these. Remember, sometimes there are enough tenths to make an extra unit. Be very careful with the columns, especially for two of the questions!

1 3.2 + 1.6

5 5.4 + 3.6

2 4.6 + 2.7

6 2.9 + 12

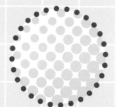

3 7.1 + 1.8

7 6.2 + 1.9

4 5.9 + 2.6

8 5 + 3.7

Subtracting decimals 2

You need to be able to subtract decimals as well as whole numbers.

1 Subtract the tenths. There are not enough tenths so we need to split up a unit to make ten extra tenths.

$$
\begin{array}{r}
{}^2\cancel{3}.{}^1 2 \\
+\ \ 1\ .\ 8 \\
\hline
4
\end{array}
$$

2 Subtract the units

$$
\begin{array}{r}
{}^2\cancel{3}.{}^1 2 \\
+\ \ 1\ .\ 8 \\
\hline
1\ .\ 4
\end{array}
$$

Now try these. Remember, sometimes there are not enough tenths so you need to make ten extra tenths by using one of the units. Be very careful to keep the decimal points lined up.

1 4.6 – 1.3

2 2.9 – 1.2

3 8.4 – 3.8

4 7 – 2.6

5 5.3 – 3.9

6 9 – 6.4

7 14 – 7.7

8 6.1 – 2.4

Addition and subtraction squares

Can you write the missing answers in each square?

Add the numbers in the left column to the numbers in the top row. Some of the answers in the first addition square have been done for you. Time how long you take to complete each square.

1

+	1.2	6	2.4	3.6
1.8		7.8		
5				
2.3	3.5			
3.4				7

3

+	2.7	3.9	4	1.8
1.6				
2.3				
7				
5.1				

Time taken — Seconds

Subtract the numbers in the left column from the numbers in the top row. Some of the answers in the first subtraction square have been done for you. Time how long you take to complete each square.

2

–	5	6	8	4
1.2		4.8		
2.3				
2.8	2.2			
3.9				0.1

4

–	6.9	7.2	8.4	9.1
1.7				
3.9				
5.6				
6.8				

Time taken — Seconds

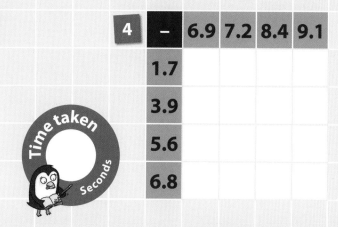

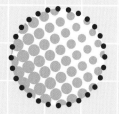

Use columns to find the answers to these questions.

1   0.6 + 0.3

2   0.6 − 0.3

3   0.9 + 0.7

4   1.4 − 0.5

5   1.6 + 2.4

6   3.6 − 1.2

7   7 + 2.4

8   6 − 2.5

9   3.9 + 5.3

10   6.4 − 1.9

11   17 + 2.4 + 0.7

12   16 − 8.3

ANSWERS

Page 3 • Addition speed

Set A

1. $9 + 4 = 13$
2. $7 + 6 = 13$
3. $8 + 8 = 16$
4. $5 + 7 = 12$
5. $6 + 8 = 14$
6. $9 + 7 = 16$
7. $4 + 8 = 12$
8. $7 + 7 = 14$
9. $3 + 9 = 12$
10. $8 + 3 = 11$
11. $12 + 4 = 16$
12. $11 + 8 = 19$
13. $13 + 3 = 16$
14. $14 + 5 = 19$
15. $12 + 6 = 18$

Set B

1. $6 + 4 = 10$
2. $5 + 6 = 11$
3. $9 + 8 = 17$
4. $3 + 7 = 10$
5. $7 + 8 = 15$
6. $2 + 7 = 9$
7. $5 + 8 = 13$
8. $9 + 7 = 16$
9. $4 + 9 = 13$
10. $9 + 3 = 12$
11. $15 + 4 = 19$
12. $17 + 8 = 25$
13. $12 + 3 = 15$
14. $16 + 5 = 21$
15. $13 + 6 = 19$

Set C

1. $9 + 9 = 18$
2. $7 + 5 = 12$
3. $8 + 3 = 11$
4. $5 + 8 = 13$
5. $6 + 2 = 8$
6. $9 + 6 = 15$
7. $4 + 5 = 9$
8. $7 + 9 = 16$
9. $3 + 8 = 11$
10. $8 + 5 = 13$
11. $12 + 5 = 17$
12. $11 + 3 = 14$
13. $13 + 6 = 19$
14. $14 + 6 = 20$
15. $12 + 9 = 21$

Page 4 • Subtraction speed

Set A

1. $9 - 3 = 6$
2. $12 - 5 = 7$
3. $16 - 9 = 7$
4. $18 - 7 = 11$
5. $8 - 5 = 3$
6. $10 - 6 = 4$
7. $11 - 4 = 7$
8. $13 - 6 = 7$
9. $15 - 9 = 6$
10. $14 - 8 = 6$
11. $21 - 7 = 14$
12. $23 - 5 = 18$
13. $27 - 9 = 18$
14. $25 - 6 = 19$
15. $22 - 8 = 14$

Set B

1. $18 - 3 = 15$
2. $13 - 5 = 8$
3. $17 - 9 = 8$
4. $11 - 7 = 4$
5. $14 - 5 = 9$
6. $9 - 6 = 3$
7. $10 - 4 = 6$
8. $12 - 6 = 6$
9. $11 - 9 = 2$
10. $23 - 8 = 15$
11. $25 - 7 = 18$
12. $29 - 5 = 24$
13. $30 - 9 = 21$
14. $22 - 6 = 16$
15. $24 - 8 = 16$

Set C

1. $9 - 5 = 4$
2. $12 - 7 = 5$
3. $16 - 4 = 12$
4. $18 - 9 = 9$
5. $8 - 8 = 0$
6. $10 - 3 = 7$
7. $11 - 8 = 3$
8. $13 - 5 = 8$
9. $15 - 7 = 8$
10. $14 - 6 = 8$
11. $21 - 3 = 18$
12. $23 - 6 = 17$
13. $27 - 11 = 16$
14. $25 - 9 = 16$
15. $22 - 7 = 15$

Page 5 • Addition squares

1.

+	8	6	7	9
5	13	11	12	14
8	16	14	15	17
7	15	13	14	16
9	17	15	16	18

2.

+	17	18	19	20
13	30	31	32	33
14	31	32	33	34
15	32	33	34	35
16	33	34	35	36

3.

+	7	9	6	8
6	13	15	12	14
8	15	17	14	16
7	14	16	13	15
9	16	18	15	17

4.

+	14	15	16	17
14	28	29	30	31
15	29	30	31	32
16	30	31	32	33
17	31	32	33	34

Brodie's Fast Five

$63 + 17 = 80$
$59 + 11 = 70$
$46 + 14 = 60$
$38 + 12 = 50$
$77 + 13 = 90$

Page 6 • Subtraction squares

1.

−	12	13	14	15
6	6	7	8	9
8	4	5	6	7
10	2	3	4	5
12	0	1	2	3

2.

−	19	21	23	20
12	7	9	11	8
6	13	15	17	14
8	11	13	15	12
14	5	7	9	6

3.

−	16	17	18	19
7	9	10	11	12
9	7	8	9	10
11	5	6	7	8
13	3	4	5	6

4.

−	17	18	19	20
11	6	7	8	9
13	4	5	6	7
15	2	3	4	5
17	0	1	2	3

Brodie's Fast Five

$50 - 13 = 37$
$100 - 17 = 83$
$80 - 16 = 64$
$60 - 26 = 34$
$70 - 15 = 55$

Page 7 • Addition and subtraction

1. $38 + 47 = 85$
2. $53 + 26 = 79$
3. $65 - 37 = 28$
4. $63 + 28 = 91$
5. $82 - 37 = 45$
6. $47 + 13 + 26 = 86$
7. $71 - 25 = 46$
8. Double $45 = 90$
9. $9 + 8 + 7 = 24$
10. $19 + 8 + 7 = 34$
11. $19 + 18 + 7 = 44$
12. $19 + 18 + 17 = 54$
13. $100 - 51 = 49$
14. $100 - 26 = 74$
15. Double $53 = 106$

Brodie's Fast Five

$100 - 72 = 28$
$100 - 84 = 16$
$100 - 52 = 48$
$100 - 64 = 36$
$100 - 32 = 68$

Page 8 • Progress Test 1

1. $9 - 5 = 4$
2. $12 + 5 = 17$
3. $16 - 7 = 9$
4. $18 + 7 = 25$
5. $10 - 5 = 5$
6. $10 + 26 = 36$
7. $11 - 7 = 4$
8. $13 + 6 = 19$
9. $21 - 9 = 12$
10. $14 + 8 = 22$
11. $21 - 6 = 15$
12. $23 + 5 = 28$
13. $22 - 9 = 13$
14. $25 + 6 = 31$
15. $20 - 8 = 12$
16. $18 + 3 = 21$
17. $22 - 5 = 17$
18. $17 + 9 = 26$
19. $23 - 7 = 16$
20. $14 + 5 = 19$
21. $21 - 6 = 15$
22. $10 - 7 = 3$
23. $12 + 6 = 18$
24. $11 + 9 = 20$
25. $23 - 0 = 23$
26. $25 + 7 = 32$
27. $29 - 12 = 17$
28. $30 - 7 = 23$
29. $22 + 6 = 28$
30. $24 + 8 = 32$
31. $13 - 5 = 8$
32. $12 + 7 = 19$
33. $16 - 9 = 7$
34. $18 + 9 = 27$
35. $18 - 6 = 12$
36. $30 - 3 = 27$
37. $13 + 8 = 21$
38. $23 - 5 = 18$
39. $15 + 7 = 22$
40. $14 - 8 = 6$
41. $21 + 9 = 30$
42. $23 - 11 = 12$
43. $27 + 11 = 38$
44. $25 - 16 = 9$
45. $22 + 7 = 29$

46.

+	12	14	16	18
11	23	25	27	29
13	25	27	29	31
15	27	29	31	33
17	29	31	33	35

47.

−	17	18	19	20
12	5	6	7	8
16	1	2	3	4
14	3	4	5	6
13	4	5	6	7

1. $16 + 84 = 100$
2. $23 + 77 = 100$
3. $19 + 81 = 100$
4. $12 + 88 = 100$
5. $44 + 56 = 100$
6. $31 + 69 = 100$
7. $25 + 75 = 100$
8. $48 + 52 = 100$
9. $37 + 63 = 100$
10. $49 + 51 = 100$
11. $36 + 64 = 100$
12. $52 + 48 = 100$
13. $33 + 67 = 100$
14. $18 + 82 = 100$
15. $29 + 71 = 100$

Brodie's Fast Five

$135 + 7 = 142$
$489 + 11 = 500$
$267 + 9 = 276$
$567 + 8 = 575$
$399 + 5 = 404$

Page 10 • Subtracting to find missing numbers

1. $100 - 77 = 23$
2. $100 - 83 = 17$
3. $100 - 75 = 25$
4. $100 - 49 = 51$
5. $100 - 67 = 33$
6. $100 - 57 = 43$
7. $100 - 47 = 53$
8. $100 - 25 = 75$
9. $100 - 19 = 81$
10. $100 - 37 = 63$
11. $100 - 27 = 73$
12. $100 - 17 = 83$
13. $100 - 41 = 59$
14. $100 - 12 = 88$
15. $100 - 61 = 39$

Brodie's Fast Five

$123 - 14 = 109$
$224 - 17 = 207$
$324 - 18 = 306$
$425 - 19 = 406$
$522 - 16 = 506$

Page 11 • Addition square

+	23	25	27	29	22	24	26	28	21
13	36	38	40	42	35	37	39	41	34
15	38	40	42	44	37	39	41	43	36
17	40	42	44	46	39	41	43	45	38
19	42	44	46	48	41	43	45	47	40
12	35	37	39	41	34	36	38	40	33
14	37	39	41	43	36	38	40	42	35
16	39	41	43	45	38	40	42	44	37
18	41	43	45	47	40	42	44	46	39
11	34	36	38	40	33	35	37	39	32

Brodie's Fast Five

$35 + 55 = 90$
$43 + 47 = 90$
$22 + 68 = 90$
$45 + 45 = 90$
$72 + 18 = 90$

Page 12 • Subtraction square

–	20	30	40	50	60	70	80	90	100
12	8	18	28	38	48	58	68	78	88
13	7	17	27	37	47	57	67	77	87
14	6	16	26	36	46	56	66	76	86
15	5	15	25	35	45	55	65	75	85
16	4	14	24	34	44	54	64	74	84
17	3	13	23	33	43	53	63	73	83
18	2	12	22	32	42	52	62	72	82
19	1	11	21	31	41	51	61	71	81
20	0	10	20	30	40	50	60	70	80

Brodie's Fast Five

$80 - 55 = 25$
$95 - 42 = 53$
$72 - 28 = 44$
$50 - 29 = 21$
$91 - 66 = 25$

Page 13 • Addition and subtraction

1. Additions:
   $28 + 73 = 101$
   $73 + 28 = 101$
   Subtractions:
   $101 - 28 = 73$
   $101 - 73 = 28$
2. Additions:
   $68 + 52 = 120$
   $52 + 68 = 120$
   Subtractions:
   $120 - 68 = 52$
   $120 - 52 = 68$
3. There are lots of numbers that add together to make 130. Check your child's answer to make sure the numbers they have used are correct.
4. There are lots of numbers that add together to make 144. Check your child's answer to make sure the numbers they have used are correct.

Brodie's Fast Five

$102 - 14 = 88$
$95 + 25 = 120$
$97 + 24 = 121$
$110 - 31 = 79$
$92 + 49 = 141$

Page 14 • Progress Test 2

Addition
1. $36 + 74 = 110$
2. $19 + 91 = 110$
3. $47 + 63 = 110$
4. $13 + 97 = 110$
5. $52 + 58 = 110$
Subtraction
6. $110 - 33 = 77$
7. $110 - 51 = 59$
8. $110 - 62 = 48$
9. $110 - 74 = 36$
10. $110 - 46 = 64$

11. There are lots of numbers that add together to make 121. Check your child's answer to make sure the numbers they have used are correct.
12. There are lots of numbers that add together to make 149. Check your child's answer to make sure the numbers they have used are correct.

Page 15 • Adding three numbers

Set A
1. $7 + 8 + 4 = 19$
2. $7 + 5 + 6 = 18$
3. $3 + 8 + 8 = 19$
4. $5 + 7 + 9 = 21$
5. $4 + 6 + 8 = 18$
6. $9 + 7 + 5 = 21$
7. $8 + 8 + 8 = 24$
8. $7 + 7 + 7 = 21$
9. $3 + 9 + 9 = 21$
10. $8 + 7 + 6 = 21$
11. $12 + 14 + 13 = 39$
12. $11 + 13 + 15 = 39$
13. $13 + 14 + 15 = 42$
14. $14 + 15 + 16 = 45$
15. $12 + 16 + 11 = 39$

Set B
1. $5 + 8 + 9 = 22$
2. $3 + 9 + 6 = 18$
3. $3 + 6 + 9 = 18$
4. $5 + 9 + 11 = 25$
5. $9 + 6 + 8 = 23$
6. $3 + 7 + 5 = 15$
7. $7 + 4 + 9 = 20$
8. $6 + 6 + 6 = 18$
9. $8 + 2 + 12 = 22$
10. $5 + 7 + 6 = 18$
11. $15 + 14 + 13 = 42$
12. $13 + 13 + 13 = 39$
13. $14 + 14 + 14 = 42$
14. $15 + 15 + 15 = 45$
15. $16 + 16 + 16 = 48$

Set C
1. $9 + 8 + 7 = 24$
2. $7 + 3 + 9 = 19$
3. $6 + 8 + 2 = 16$
4. $12 + 7 + 9 = 28$
5. $5 + 6 + 11 = 22$
6. $2 + 12 + 12 = 26$
7. $5 + 8 + 6 = 19$
8. $9 + 2 + 8 = 19$
9. $7 + 9 + 6 = 22$
10. $12 + 12 + 6 = 30$
11. $16 + 14 + 16 = 46$
12. $17 + 13 + 15 = 45$
13. $16 + 14 + 20 = 50$
14. $25 + 15 + 35 = 75$
15. $25 + 25 + 25 = 75$

Page 16 • Addition and subtraction

Set A
1. $7 + 8 - 6 = 9$
2. $7 + 9 - 5 = 11$
3. $12 + 8 - 7 = 13$
4. $15 + 7 - 4 = 18$
5. $14 + 6 - 9 = 11$
6. $9 + 7 - 8 = 8$
7. $8 + 8 - 4 = 12$
8. $12 + 7 - 5 = 14$
9. $11 + 9 - 6 = 14$
10. $18 + 7 - 9 = 16$
11. $12 + 14 - 4 = 22$
12. $12 + 13 - 8 = 17$
13. $16 + 14 - 12 = 18$
14. $25 + 15 - 14 = 26$
15. $12 + 18 - 4 = 26$

Set B
1. $17 + 8 - 9 = 16$
2. $7 + 19 - 8 = 18$
3. $12 + 18 - 11 = 19$
4. $12 + 6 - 8 = 10$
5. $14 + 16 - 15 = 15$
6. $19 + 7 - 10 = 16$
7. $8 + 18 - 12 = 14$
8. $19 + 9 - 5 = 23$
9. $15 + 9 - 16 = 8$
10. $18 + 17 - 9 = 26$
11. $16 + 14 - 4 = 26$
12. $17 + 13 - 8 = 22$
13. $12 + 18 - 12 = 18$
14. $35 + 35 - 14 = 56$
15. $22 + 22 - 44 = 0$

Set C
1. $7 + 18 - 9 = 16$
2. $12 + 9 - 5 = 16$
3. $14 + 8 - 7 = 15$
4. $15 + 8 - 4 = 19$
5. $16 + 6 - 8 = 14$
6. $19 + 17 - 11 = 25$
7. $14 + 14 - 15 = 13$
8. $12 + 12 - 5 = 19$
9. $11 + 11 - 8 = 14$
10. $18 + 18 - 13 = 23$
11. $13 + 13 - 11 = 15$
12. $15 + 15 - 12 = 18$
13. $16 + 16 - 12 = 20$
14. $45 + 45 - 28 = 62$
15. $55 + 55 - 18 = 92$

Page 17 • Adding multiples of ten

Set A
1. $70 + 40 = 110$
2. $60 + 60 = 120$
3. $90 + 80 = 170$
4. $30 + 90 = 120$
5. $80 + 80 = 160$
6. $60 + 70 = 130$
7. $50 + 80 = 130$
8. $90 + 70 = 160$
9. $30 + 80 = 110$
10. $40 + 60 = 100$
11. $130 + 140 = 270$
12. $110 + 180 = 290$
13. $180 + 130 = 310$
14. $190 + 160 = 350$
15. $180 + 180 = 360$

Set B
1. 80 + 30 = 110
2. 70 + 60 = 130
3. 120 + 60 = 180
4. 40 + 70 = 110
5. 70 + 80 = 150
6. 110 + 90 = 200
7. 150 + 50 = 200
8. 120 + 80 = 200
9. 60 + 140 = 200
10. 130 + 70 = 200
11. 120 + 180 = 300
12. 170 + 130 = 300
13. 140 + 160 = 300
14. 110 + 190 = 300
15. 150 + 150 = 300

Set C
1. 90 + 90 = 180
2. 70 + 70 = 140
3. 80 + 80 = 160
4. 60 + 60 = 120
5. 110 + 110 = 220
6. 150 + 150 = 300
7. 120 + 120 = 240
8. 140 + 140 = 280
9. 160 + 160 = 320
10. 130 + 130 = 260
11. 170 + 170 = 340
12. 190 + 190 = 380
13. 180 + 180 = 360
14. 200 + 200 = 400
15. 250 + 250 = 500

Page 18 • Subtracting multiples of ten

Set A
1. 190 – 30 = 160
2. 170 – 110 = 60
3. 160 – 90 = 70
4. 180 – 90 = 90
5. 120 – 50 = 70
6. 130 – 80 = 50
7. 110 – 40 = 70
8. 270 – 60 = 210
9. 350 – 90 = 260
10. 720 – 80 = 640
11. 210 – 70 = 140
12. 480 – 150 = 330
13. 660 – 90 = 570
14. 830 – 60 = 770
15. 910 – 80 = 830

Set B
1. 180 – 30 = 150
2. 230 – 50 = 180
3. 490 – 110 = 380
4. 620 – 70 = 550
5. 930 – 50 = 880
6. 710 – 60 = 650
7. 550 – 80 = 470
8. 360 – 70 = 290
9. 540 – 90 = 450
10. 460 – 80 = 380
11. 250 – 70 = 180
12. 740 – 150 = 590
13. 360 – 180 = 180
14. 820 – 160 = 660
15. 900 – 450 = 450

Set C
1. 190 – 60 = 130
2. 140 – 70 = 70
3. 160 – 80 = 80
4. 120 – 60 = 60
5. 180 – 90 = 90
6. 220 – 110 = 110
7. 240 – 120 = 120
8. 480 – 240 = 240
9. 660 – 330 = 330
10. 840 – 420 = 420
11. 400 – 120 = 280
12. 600 – 160 = 440
13. 900 – 340 = 560
14. 800 – 370 = 430
15. 500 – 250 = 250

Page 19 • Adding and subtracting hundreds with three-digit numbers

Adding
1. 479 + 300 = 779
2. 389 + 200 = 589
3. 624 + 400 = 1024
4. 438 + 300 = 738
5. 842 + 500 = 1342
6. 269 + 600 = 869
7. 835 + 500 = 1335
8. 442 + 400 = 842
9. 583 + 300 = 883
10. 679 + 800 = 1479

Subtracting
1. 747 – 200 = 547
2. 832 – 500 = 332
3. 916 – 400 = 516
4. 803 – 600 = 203
5. 932 – 900 = 32
6. 891 – 500 = 391
7. 789 – 600 = 189
8. 666 – 300 = 366
9. 713 – 400 = 313
10. 863 – 200 = 663

Brodie's Fast Five
297 + 400 = 697
765 + 500 = 1265
826 – 200 = 626
1000 – 420 = 580
913 + 400 = 1313

Page 20 • Progress Test 3
1. 12 + 8 – 6 = 14
2. 14 + 9 – 5 = 18
3. 12 + 8 – 13 = 7
4. 26 + 7 – 4 = 29
5. 24 + 8 – 9 = 23
6. 26 + 7 – 8 = 25
7. 38 + 8 – 14 = 32
8. 32 + 7 – 15 = 24
9. 35 + 9 – 6 = 38
10. 48 + 7 – 9 = 46
11. 130 + 80 = 210
12. 160 + 140 = 300
13. 130 + 170 = 300
14. 320 + 180 = 500
15. 270 + 150 = 420
16. 340 – 110 = 230
17. 240 – 160 = 80
18. 480 – 190 = 290
19. 520 – 330 = 190
20. 710 – 420 = 290
21. 564 – 200 = 364
22. 888 – 400 = 488
23. 907 – 300 = 607
24. 742 – 500 = 242
25. 635 – 300 = 335

Page 22 • Addition in columns
1. 72 + 23 = 95
2. 43 + 35 = 78
3. 31 + 28 = 59
4. 56 + 35 = 91
5. 67 + 23 = 90
6. 44 + 32 = 76
7. 39 + 26 = 65
8. 64 + 18 = 82
9. 51 + 35 = 86
10. 47 + 38 = 85

Brodie's Fast Five
57 + 30 = 87
57 + 130 = 187
57 + 230 = 287
57 + 330 = 387
57 + 430 = 487

Page 23 • Additions with answers over 100
1. 84 + 38 = 122
2. 73 + 42 = 115
3. 95 + 69 = 164
4. 75 + 75 = 150

Brodie's Fast Five
6 + 13 = 19
6 + 13 = 19
12 + 7 = 19
12 + 7 = 19
9 + 10 = 19

Page 25 • Subtraction in columns
1. 86 – 42 = 44
2. 98 – 56 = 42
3. 47 – 31 = 16
4. 69 – 22 = 47
5. 75 – 34 = 41
6. 51 – 26 = 25
7. 85 – 48 = 37
8. 93 – 62 = 31
9. 90 – 56 = 34
10. 62 – 37 = 25

Brodie's Fast Five
350 – 5 = 345
350 – 15 = 335
350 – 25 = 325
4350 – 35 = 315
350 – 45 = 305

Page 26 • Progress Test 4
1. 53 + 32 = 85
2. 69 + 27 = 96
3. 74 + 25 = 99
4. 56 + 27 = 83
5. 89 – 28 = 61
6. 78 – 35 = 43
7. 63 – 49 = 14
8. 81 – 57 = 24
9. 53 + 29 = 82
10. 82 – 27 = 55

Page 27 • Adding three-digit numbers 1
1. 234 + 123 = 357
2. 561 + 217 = 778
3. 472 + 326 = 798
4. 743 + 154 = 897
5. 312 + 312 = 624
6. 436 + 128 = 564
7. 263 + 263 = 526
8. 180 + 180 = 360

Page 28 • Adding three-digit numbers 2
1. 386 + 295 = 681
2. 542 + 387 = 929
3. 472 + 472 = 944
4. 743 + 444 = 1187
5. 862 + 379 = 1241
6. 750 + 750 = 1500
7. 699 + 699 = 1398
8. 947 + 378 = 1325

Page 29 • Adding three-digit numbers and two-digit numbers
1. 475 + 63 = 538
2. 637 + 79 = 716
3. 525 + 98 = 623
4. 76 + 632 = 708
5. 469 + 28 = 497
6. 84 + 862 = 946
7. 74 + 577 = 651
8. 957 + 89 = 1046

Page 30 • More subtraction in columns 1
1. 586 – 192 = 394
2. 756 – 234 = 522
3. 925 – 367 = 558
4. 847 – 264 = 583
5. 946 – 387 = 559
6. 738 – 499 = 239

Page 31 • More subtraction in columns 2
1. 597 – 146 = 451
2. 871 – 236 = 635
3. 952 – 417 = 535
4. 508 – 137 = 371
5. 836 – 475 = 361
6. 627 – 253 = 374
7. 624 – 179 = 445
8. 835 – 266 = 569
9. 925 – 468 = 457

Brodie's Fast Five
200 – 2 = 198
200 – 12 = 188
200 – 22 = 178
200 – 32 = 168
200 – 42 = 158

Page 32 • Progress Test 5
1. 572 + 315 = 887
2. 617 + 239 = 856
3. 746 + 88 = 834
4. 869 + 375 = 1244
5. 468 – 214 = 254
6. 583 – 329 = 254
7. 612 – 148 = 464
8. 817 – 293 = 524
9. 929 – 359 = 570

Page 33 • Adding four-digit numbers

1. 3472 + 2914 = 6386
2. 5925 + 3172 = 9097
3. 4628 + 2560 = 7188
4. 3945 + 1872 = 5817
5. 6823 + 5749 = 12572
6. 8750 + 8750 = 17500

Page 34 • Subtracting four-digit numbers

1. 6759 − 2345 = 4414
2. 7399 − 2681 = 4718
3. 8645 − 3760 = 4885
4. 5478 − 2888 = 2590
5. 9324 − 4687 = 4637
6. 7309 − 5624 = 1685

Page 35 • Subtracting just from hundreds

1. 600 − 192 = 408
2. 800 − 234 = 566
3. 700 − 367 = 333
4. 900 − 264 = 636
5. 500 − 387 = 113
6. 800 − 499 = 301

Page 36 • Subtracting just from thousands

1. 5000 − 2361 = 2639
2. 7000 − 3982 = 3018
3. 8000 − 4738 = 3262
4. 6000 − 3209 = 2791
5. 9000 − 2754 = 6246
6. 8000 − 4994 = 3006

Page 37 • Addition and subtraction

1. 5576 + 3940 = 9516 km
2. 9516 + 8765 = 18281 km
3. 5576 − 3940 = 1636 km
4. 9516 − 8765 = 751 km

Brodie's Fast Five

Double 62 = 124
Double 78 = 156
Double 99 = 198
Double 170 = 340
Double 250 = 500

Page 38 • Progress Test 6

1. 697 + 315 = 1012
2. 892 + 768 = 1660
3. 929 + 88 = 1017
4. 3456 + 6789 = 10245
5. 576 − 214 = 362
6. 710 − 329 = 381
7. 2468 − 1708 = 760
8. 8000 − 3245 = 4755
9. 9000 − 4359 = 4641

Page 39 • Adding decimals

0.1 + 0.9 = 1
0.2 + 0.8 = 1
0.3 + 0.7 = 1
0.4 + 0.6 = 1
0.5 + 0.5 = 1
0.6 + 0.4 = 1
0.7 + 0.3 = 1
0.8 + 0.2 = 1
0.9 + 0.1 = 1

Set A
1. 0.2 + 0.4 = 0.6
2. 7 + 1.6 = 8.6
3. 0.8 + 0.1 = 0.9
4. 0.5 + 0.3 = 0.8
5. 0.6 + 0.8 = 1.4
6. 2.4 + 7 = 9.4
7. 1.4 + 0.8 = 2.2
8. 0.7 + 0.7 = 1.4

Set B
1. 0.6 + 0.4 = 1
2. 1.5 + 0.6 = 2.1
3. 0.9 + 0.8 = 1.7
4. 1.3 + 0.5 = 1.8
5. 0.7 + 0.8 = 1.5
6. 0.2 + 0.7 = 0.9
7. 0.5 + 0.8 = 1.3
8. 0.9 + 0.7 = 1.6

Set C
1. 0.9 + 0.2 = 1.1
2. 0.7 + 1.5 = 2.2
3. 0.8 + 0.3 = 1.1
4. 0.5 + 1.8 = 2.3
5. 1.6 + 1.2 = 2.8
6. 1.9 + 0.6 = 2.5
7. 1.4 + 0.5 = 1.9
8. 1.7 + 0.9 = 2.6

Page 40 • Subtracting decimals

1 − 0.7 = 0.3
1 − 0.3 = 0.7
1 − 0.8 = 0.2
1 − 0.9 = 0.1
1 − 0.6 = 0.4
1 − 0.4 = 0.6
1 − 0.2 = 0.8
1 − 0.5 = 0.5
1 − 0.1 = 0.9

Set A
1. 1.2 − 0.4 = 0.8
2. 0.9 − 0.3 = 0.6
3. 1.5 − 0.8 = 0.7
4. 0.8 − 0.4 = 0.4
5. 1.2 − 0.7 = 0.5
6. 0.7 − 0.3 = 0.4
7. 1.6 − 0.9 = 0.7
8. 2.1 − 0.3 = 1.8

Set B
1. 0.6 − 0.4 = 0.2
2. 1.7 − 0.9 = 0.8
3. 2.3 − 0.4 = 1.9
4. 1.8 − 1.2 = 0.6
5. 0.9 − 0.1 = 0.8
6. 3.2 − 0.8 = 2.4
7. 4.5 − 0.7 = 3.8
8. 3.7 − 1.4 = 2.3

Set C
1. 0.9 − 0.2 = 0.7
2. 1.6 − 0.8 = 0.8
3. 2.3 − 1.5 = 0.8
4. 3.4 − 1.6 = 1.8
5. 2.5 − 0.8 = 1.7
6. 3.2 − 1.5 = 1.7
7. 5.5 − 2.7 = 2.8
8. 4.2 − 2.3 = 1.9

Page 41 • Adding decimals 2

1. 3.2 + 1.6 = 4.8
2. 4.6 + 2.7 = 7.3
3. 7.1 + 1.8 = 8.9
4. 5.9 + 2.6 = 8.5
5. 5.4 + 3.6 = 9
6. 2.9 + 12 = 14.9
7. 6.2 + 1.9 = 8.1
8. 5 + 3.7 = 8.7

Page 42 • Subtracting decimals 2

1. 4.6 − 1.3 = 3.3
2. 2.9 − 1.2 = 1.7
3. 8.4 − 3.8 = 4.6
4. 7 − 2.6 = 4.4
5. 5.3 − 3.9 = 1.4
6. 9 − 6.4 = 2.6
7. 14 − 7.7 = 6.3
8. 6.1 − 2.4 = 3.7

Page 43 • Addition and subtraction squares

1.

+	1.2	6	2.4	3.6
1.8	3	7.8	4.2	5.4
5	6.2	11	7.4	8.6
2.3	3.5	8.3	4.7	5.9
3.4	4.6	9.4	5.8	7

2.

+	2.7	3.9	4	1.8
1.6	4.3	5.5	5.6	3.4
2.3	5	6.2	6.3	4.1
7	9.7	10.9	11	8.8
5.1	7.8	9	9.1	6.9

3.

−	5	6	8	4
1.2	3.8	4.8	6.8	2.8
2.3	2.7	3.7	5.7	1.7
2.8	2.2	3.2	5.2	1.2
3.9	1.1	2.1	4.1	0.1

4.

−	6.9	7.2	8.4	9.1
1.7	5.2	5.5	6.7	7.4
3.9	3	3.3	4.5	5.2
5.6	1.3	1.6	2.8	3.5
6.8	0.1	0.4	1.6	2.3

Page 44 • Progress Test 7

1. 0.6 + 0.3 = 0.9
2. 0.6 − 0.3 = 0.3
3. 0.9 + 0.7 = 1.6
4. 1.4 − 0.5 = 0.9
5. 1.6 + 2.4 = 4
6. 3.6 − 1.2 = 2.4
7. 7 + 2.4 = 9.4
8. 6 − 2.5 = 3.5
9. 3.9 + 5.3 = 9.2
10. 6.4 − 1.9 = 4.5
11. 17 + 2.4 + 0.7 = 20.1
12. 16 − 8.3 = 7.7